Spring make and do activity book

igloobooks

Contents

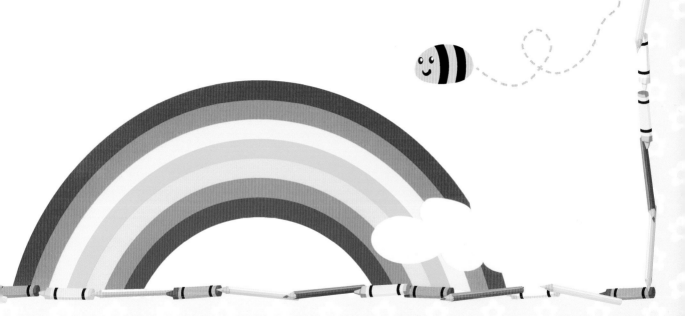

Spring Garlands

Decorate your den with these fun flower garlands.

Remember!
Always ask an adult to help when using scissors.

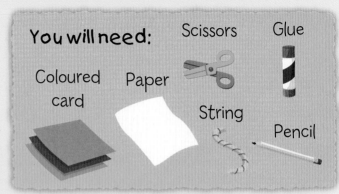

You will need:

Coloured card   Paper   Scissors   Glue   String   Pencil

Step 1

Draw a flower shape onto a piece of paper. Carefully cut out the flower, then trace around it onto several pieces of coloured card.

Step 2

Repeat the flower shape as many times as you like, but be sure to have an even number. Carefully cut out the card flowers.

Step 3

Take two flowers and glue them together with the string sandwiched between them. Repeat this step until it reaches the length you want.

Super Sponge Rainbow

Create big and beautiful rainbows to brighten up your bedroom.

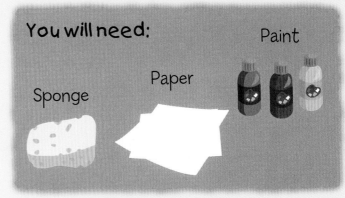

You will need:

Sponge

Paper

Paint

Step 1

Squeeze a small blob of red paint onto the end of the sponge. Then, squeeze a blob of orange, yellow, green, blue and purple paint in a line, as shown.

Step 2

Sweep the sponge across the paper in an arc shape, making a big rainbow.

Hand Puppet Pal

Create a cute bunny puppet, perfect for playtime.

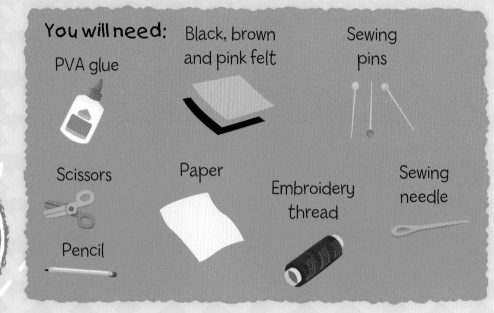

You will need:

PVA glue

Black, brown and pink felt

Sewing pins

Scissors

Paper

Embroidery thread

Sewing needle

Pencil

Remember!
Always ask an adult to help when using scissors, needles or pins.

Step 1

Draw a bunny shape, as shown, onto a piece of white paper and cut it out. Make sure it's bigger than your hand.

Step 2

Pin the paper bunny shape onto a piece of brown felt. Cut the shape out, then repeat to get a second bunny.

Step 3

Place the felt shapes directly on top of one another and pin them together. Then, sew the edges together, leaving the bottom edge open.

Step 4

Turn your sewn bunny inside-out. If needed, use a pencil to push out the ears.

Step 5

Cut a small triangle and two long teardrop shapes from the pink felt, and two small circles from the black felt. These will be the bunny's eyes, nose and ears.

Step 6

Carefully glue the eyes, nose and ears onto your bunny, as shown, then wait for it to dry.

Moo Meadow

The baby animals are playing in the flower meadow.
Can you spot ten differences between the two pictures below?

a

b

Answers on page 96

Happy Lambs

Baa! It's a sunny day in Lucy Lamb's field.
Can you work out which shadow belongs to Lucy?

Lucy

Bunny Mischief

One of these mischievous bunnies has gobbled all the carrots.
Follow the clues to work out which one has a full tummy.

The bunny:
- has a yellow bobble on his hat
- has hearts on his top
- is wearing a purple top

Answers on page 96

Piñata Party

Create an egg-cellent piñata, perfect for a springtime party.

You will need:

A round balloon

PVA glue

Strips of newspaper

Paint

Water

Sweets

Paintbrush

String

Step 1

Blow up a round balloon and tie a knot in the end.

Step 2

To make the papier mâché paste, mix two parts PVA glue to one part water in a bowl. Dip the newspaper strips into the paste and cover the balloon. Make sure you leave a hole at the top, near the knot.

Step 3

Once dry, cover the balloon with another layer of newspaper and leave it to dry. Then, repeat the process for a final time with one more layer of newspaper.

Step 4

Once fully dry, ask an adult to pop the balloon inside and remove it.

Step 5

Paint your piñata in one colour all over. Once dry, paint a funky pattern over the top.

Step 6

Ask an adult to make two holes at the top, as shown. Thread string through the holes and tie a knot at the top.

Step 6

Fill the piñata with sweets, then attach it to the ceiling with a piece of sticky tape.

Spring Strings

Make some funky spring strings to hang above your bed.

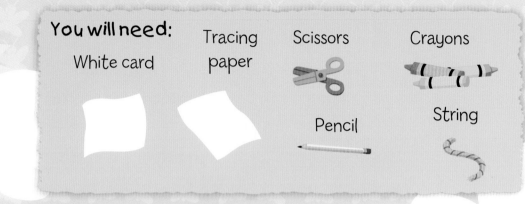

You will need:

White card   Tracing paper   Scissors   Crayons

Pencil   String

Step 1

Trace the shapes above onto white card,
then ask an adult to cut them out.

Step 2

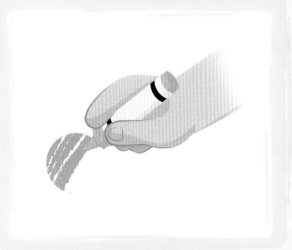

Use crayons to decorate the shapes in any way you like. Remember to decorate the backs, too.

Step 3

Ask an adult to make holes at the top and bottom of each shape.

Step 4

Thread string through the front of the top hole, then through the back of the bottom hole. Tie a knot at the bottom of each shape to stop it from sliding down.

Step 5

Continue to add more shapes to the string until it has reached the length you want.

Fluttery Butterfly

The pattern on a butterfly's wings is always symmetrical. Finish the beautiful butterfly below by colouring in her wings.

Which Weather?

There are lots of different types of weather in spring.
Can you work out which item matches each type of weather?

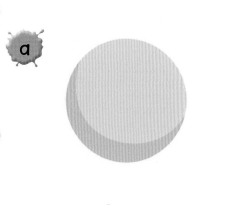

a

Sunny

1

Umbrella

b

Rainy

2

Coat

c

Snowy

3

Hat

Answers on page 96

Door Decoration

Make this pretty egg wreath to hang on your bedroom door.

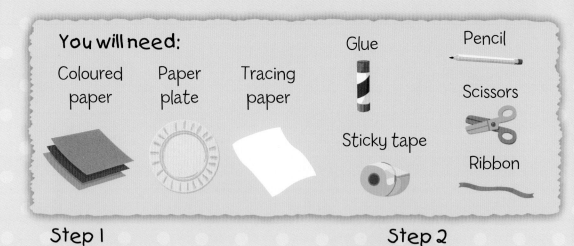

You will need:

Coloured paper

Paper plate

Tracing paper

Glue

Sticky tape

Pencil

Scissors

Ribbon

Step 1

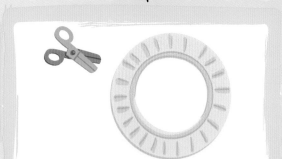

Ask an adult to cut out the middle from the paper plate.

Step 2

Draw 12-15 egg shapes onto the coloured paper, then ask an adult to cut them out.

Step 3

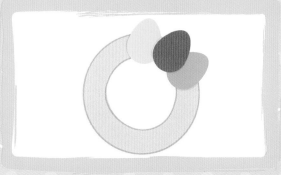

Glue the egg shapes onto the back of the paper plate, overlapping as shown.

Step 4

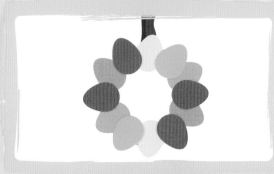

Cut a length of ribbon. Attach it to the back of the wreath in a loop with sticky tape.

16

Rainbow Blower

Create pretty rainbows with this magnificent make.

Step 1

Paint your cardboard tube blue all over. Once dry, paint white clouds over the top.

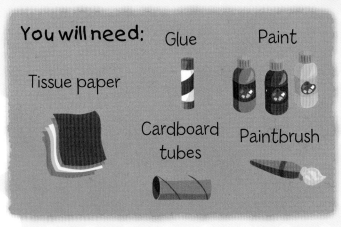

You will need: Tissue paper, Glue, Paint, Cardboard tubes, Paintbrush

Step 2

To make your streamers, ask an adult to cut strips of tissue paper in red, orange, yellow, green, blue and purple or pink.

Step 3

Glue one end of each tissue paper strip, then stick them around the inside rim of the cardboard tube.

Step 4

Blow into the tube to make the rainbow streamers fly in all directions.

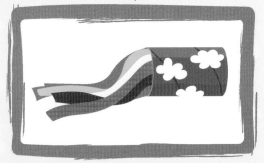

Sweet Sheep

Make your own soft and fuzzy pom-pom sheep.

Step 1

Ask an adult to help you cut two circles, about 8 cm across, out of cardboard. Then, cut a hole in the middle of each circle, about 3 cm across, to make a donut shape.

You will need:

Cardboard

Black pipe cleaners

Scissors

Googly eyes

White wool

PVA glue

Black craft foam

Step 2

Lay the circles directly on top of one another, then thread the wool through the middle hole. Wrap the wool around the edge of the discs until the hole is filled.

Step 3

Ask an adult to put the scissors in between the two cardboard discs and cut the wool around the outer edge.

Step 4

Pull the two discs apart slightly and thread a long length of wool between them.

Step 5

Tie the ends of the wool into a tight knot. Repeat the knot to make sure it's secure.

Step 6

Once tied, ask an adult to cut and remove the cardboard discs from the wool.

Step 7

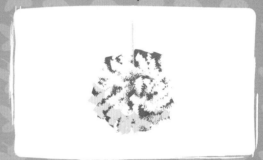

Trim the pom-pom to remove any bits of wool that stick out above the rest, so that you get a circular shape.

Step 8

Draw the shape shown above onto black craft foam and ask an adult to cut it out. Glue on the googly eyes, then glue the head to the pom-pom.

Step 9

To make the legs, thread the pipe cleaners through the middle of the body, at the front and back, then fold the ends up to make feet.

Fluffy Friends

Some animals jump, some animals slide and some animals fly.
Can you guess which cute character is the odd one out?

Eggs for Everyone

The animals can't wait to eat their chocolate eggs. Match the
patterns to work out which egg belongs to each character.

Answers on page 96

Farm Fun

It's a busy morning on the farm and the animals are having lots of fun. Decorate this picture with your pens or crayons.

Super Stamps

Personalise cards and gift wrap with this cute potato stamp.

Step 1

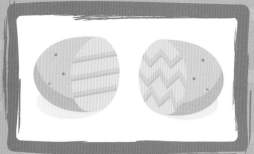

Ask an adult to cut a potato in half and cut a pretty pattern into it, about 1 cm deep into the potato.

You will need:

Paper

A potato

Paint

Paintbrush

Step 2

Paint the cut-out design with bright colours.

Step 3

Press the painted side of the potato firmly onto paper. Lift it away to reveal a beautiful painted egg.

Top tip!
To reuse the stamps, always wash off the previous paint colour to avoid mixing.

Egg Hunt

Play this game to see who finds the most hidden eggs.

Step 1

Draw ten patterned egg shapes onto card.

You will need:

Felt-tip pens or pencils

Card

Pencil

Scissors

Step 2

Decorate the eggs with felt-tip pens. Make them as bright as possible.

Step 3

Ask an adult to cut out the eggs.

How to play:

Hide the eggs around the house or garden. Each player has ten minutes to find the hidden eggs. Each player must then add up the numbers on the backs of the eggs they've found. The player with the highest number wins.

Step 4

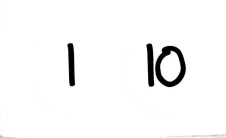

1   10

Write the numbers 1-10 on the back of each egg.

Bunny Bookmarks

Never lose your page again with this brilliant bunny bookmark.

You will need:

Card

Scissors

Pencil

Tracing paper

Felt-tip pens

Step 1

Trace the bunny shape onto a piece of card, then ask an adult to cut it out.

Step 2

Add some cute details to the bunny, as shown. Why not add a bow tie and white tummy, too?

Flower Power

Make a fun flower crown, perfect for playing kings and queens.

Step 1

Ask an adult to cut two strips of green paper long enough to fit around your head. Sticky tape them together.

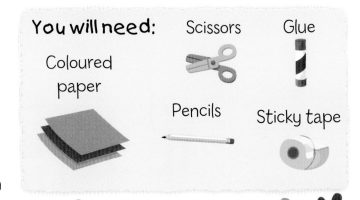

You will need:

Coloured paper

Scissors

Glue

Pencils

Sticky tape

Step 2

Draw flower shapes onto the coloured paper, leaf shapes onto the green paper, and circles onto the yellow paper. Ask an adult to cut them out.

Step 3

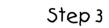

Stick the yellow circles to the top of the flower shapes. Then, stick the green leaves underneath as shown.

Step 4

Glue the flowers to the green headband strip, about 2 cm apart.

Step 5

Wrap it around your head, then sticky tape the ends together.

Magnificent Maze

This bumblebee is trying to get back to his hive.
Can you help him by guiding him through the maze?

Start

Finish

Answer on page 96

Spring Wreath

This wreath is looking a little bare. Create a cool design for it, then decorate the picture using pens or crayons.

Spring Sun Catcher

Create a rainbow with this wonderful window sun catcher.

Step 1

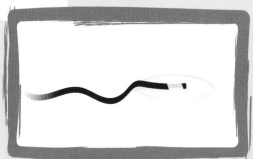

Ask an adult to cut a long length of ribbon and sticky tape it to the plastic lid. This will allow you to hang it up.

You will need:

A clear plastic lid from a yogurt pot

Tissue paper

Scissors

PVA glue

Sticky tape

Ribbon

Paintbrush

Step 2

Ask an adult to cut the tissue paper into strips and a variety of different shapes.

Step 3

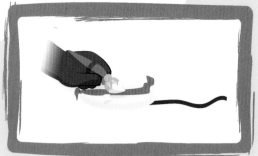

Glue the pieces of tissue paper to the lid, in any way you like, to create a unique design.

Step 4

Leave the sun catcher to dry, then hang it up in the window for the sun to stream through.

Hanging Hot-air Balloon

Make a funky hot-air balloon to decorate your bedroom wall with.

You will need:

White and brown paper

Scissors

Felt-tip pens

Glue

Tracing paper

Pencil

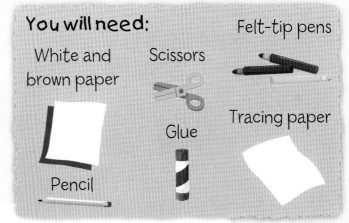

Step 1

Draw the shape shown above onto a piece of white paper and then cut it out.

Step 2

Draw the shape shown above onto a piece of brown paper and cut it out.

Step 3

Cut two small same-sized strips from the white paper, then assemble and glue the pieces together, as shown, to create a hot-air balloon shape.

Step 4

Decorate your hot-air balloon with felt-tip pens.

29

Cute Cupcakes

Make twelve tasty cupcakes for your spring picnic.

You will need:

100 g
Soft butter

100 g
Self-raising
flour

2 Eggs

100 g
Caster sugar

150 g
Icing sugar

Food
colouring

Sprinkles

3 tbsp
Water

Cupcake
cases

Wooden
spoon

Spoon

Mixing bowl

Cooling rack

Remember!
Always ask an adult to help you when using the oven.

Step 1

Put the oven on to
gas mark 4/180°C/356°F.

Step 2

Mix together the butter and sugar until creamy. Next, crack the eggs into the mixture and add the flour.

Step 3

Mix the ingredients together, then spoon the mixture into cupcake cases, until half full.

Step 4

Bake for 10-15 minutes. To check whether they're cooked, ask an adult to press the top gently. The cake should spring back up.

Step 5

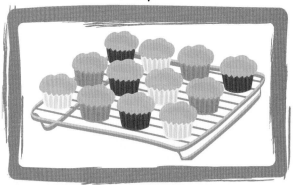

Once cooked, ask an adult to place the cakes onto a cooling rack to let them cool.

Step 6

To make the icing, mix together the icing sugar and water. To make it a fun colour, add a drop of food colouring into the mix.

Step 7

Once the cupcakes are cool, use a small spoon to spread the icing over the tops. Whilst the icing is still wet, add rainbow sprinkles for added decoration.

Wonderful Wildlife

There's lots of wildlife to spot at springtime.
Can you work out which small grid matches the big grid?

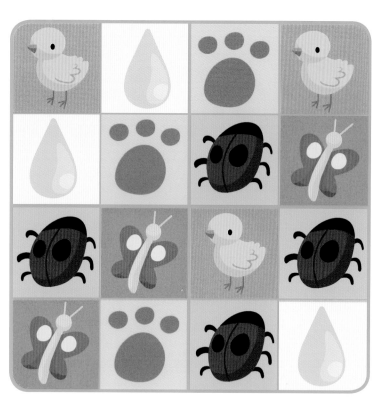

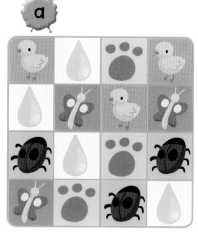

a

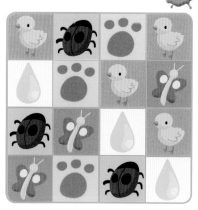

b

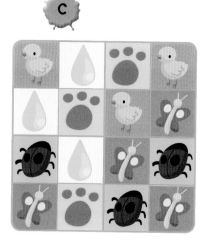

c

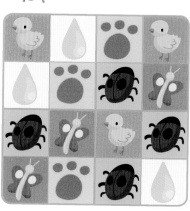

d

Answer on page 96

Broken Eggshells

Uh-oh! All the chocolate eggs are broken. Can you put them back together by matching the broken halves?

Spring Garden

Get creative and make this pretty plate garden.

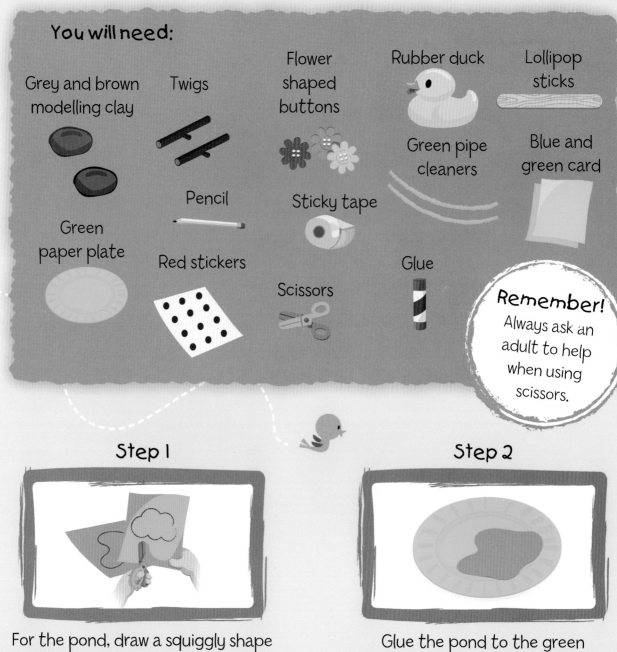

You will need:

Grey and brown modelling clay

Twigs

Flower shaped buttons

Rubber duck

Lollipop sticks

Green pipe cleaners

Blue and green card

Green paper plate

Pencil

Sticky tape

Red stickers

Scissors

Glue

Remember! Always ask an adult to help when using scissors.

Step 1

For the pond, draw a squiggly shape onto the blue card. For the tree canopy, draw two cloud shapes onto the green card. Cut out the shapes.

Step 2

Glue the pond to the green paper plate. If you don't have a green paper plate, you can use a white paper plate and paint it green.

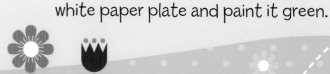

Step 3

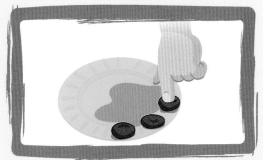

Roll small balls of grey modelling clay to make stepping stones for the path. Gently press them down onto the plate, next to the pond.

Step 4

Roll the brown modelling clay into a sausage shape. Press it onto the other side of the pond to make a flower bed.

Step 5

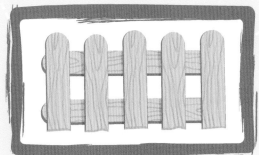

Ask an adult to cut two lollipop sticks in half. Glue the pieces onto two more sticks to make a fence. When it's dry, push it into the back of the flower bed.

Step 6

Stick two twigs on the back of the green tree shapes using sticky tape. Add red stickers for apples. Then stick the trees into the flower bed next to the fence.

Step 7

Cut a pipe cleaner into three 6 cm pieces, then thread them through each button hole. Stick the flowers into the flower bed.

Step 8

Place the rubber duck in the pond. Now you have your own little spring garden.

Cool Creepy-crawlies

There are lots of different creepy-crawlies in the garden at springtime. Can you spot all the critters in the picture?

 7 bumblebees

6 beetles

 5 butterflies

4 spiders

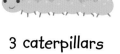 3 caterpillars

 2 spotty bugs

Answers on page 96

Jumping Jigsaw

Boing, boing! The bunnies are bouncing around in the sunshine. Can you work out where each jigsaw piece fits in the picture?

Answers on page 96

Pop-up Garden

Create a spring display with this pretty pop-up scene.

Step 1

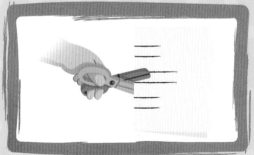

Fold the card in half. Ask an adult to cut six slits in the middle, over the fold. The two centre slits should be longer than the rest.

You will need:

Card

Paper

Scissors

Pencils or crayons

Glue

Step 2

Open the card and push the areas between cuts, so that they pop up.

Step 3

Close the card, then glue a piece of paper around the outside to disguise the holes in the card.

Step 4

Draw three flowers shapes and decorate them. Ask an adult to cut them out.

Step 5

Glue the flowers to the pop-ups, then draw grass, leaves and a sun to finish.

Bunny Napkin

Fold an adorable little bunny to sit at the dinner table with you.

Step 1

Fold the napkin into quarters horizontally.

You will need: Paper napkin

Step 2

Bring the outer edges downwards, as shown.

Step 3

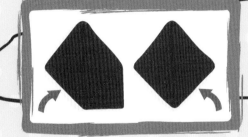

Fold the bottom two corners into the middle to create a diamond shape.

Step 4

Fig. 1   Fig. 2

Fold the corners into the centre (Fig. 1) to make a kite shape (Fig. 2).

Step 5

Fig. 1

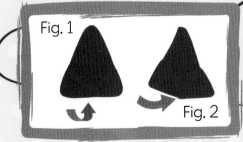

Fig. 2

Turn it upside down, then fold the bottom corner behind (Fig. 1). Next, tuck one corner into the pocket of the opposite side (Fig. 2).

Step 6

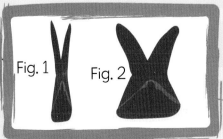

Fig. 1   Fig. 2

Turn the napkin 90 degrees to face you, as shown (Fig. 1). Pull the ears apart, then open out the base (Fig. 2).

Pretty Paper Chains

These bright paper chains are the perfect party decoration.

Step 1

Ask an adult to cut 50 strips, about 2 cm wide and 12 cm long, from the different coloured paper.

You will need:

Coloured paper

Scissors

Sticky tape

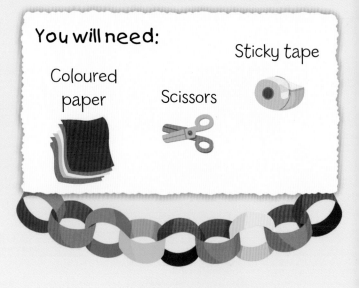

Step 2

Sticky tape the ends of one strip together to make a loop.

Step 3

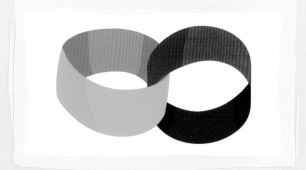

Thread another strip of paper through the first loop, then sticky tape the ends together to make another loop.

Step 4

Repeat step 3, adding more loops, until you have made a chain long enough to hang up.

Lovely Lacy Sheep

Make an entire flock of these cute paper doily sheep friends.

Step 1

Copy the head shape shown above onto black paper, then ask an adult to cut it out. Next, cut out two strips from the black paper for legs.

You will need:

Paper doilies   Googly eyes   Scissors

Pencil   Glue   Black paper

Step 2

Stick the googly eyes onto the head shape. Next, stick the head onto the front of the doily and the legs onto the back.

Step 3

Repeat steps 1-2 to make your fun flock of sheep.

Beautiful Butterfly

This beautiful butterfly is quick and easy to make yourself.

Step 1

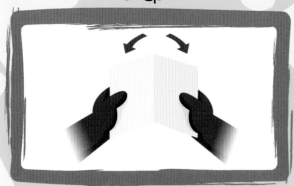

Fold your paper in half.

Step 2

On one half of the paper, paint a big colourful butterfly wing.

Step 3

Whilst the paint is still wet, fold your paper in half and press down. When you open it out again, you will have a symmetrical butterfly.

Step 4

Paint the butterfly's body.

Top tip! Create unique butterflies using different colours and patterns.

Creepy-crawlies Rock

Turn garden pebbles into all kinds of cool creatures.

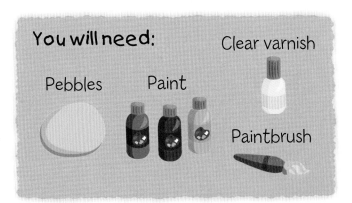

Clear varnish

Pebbles   Paint

Paintbrush

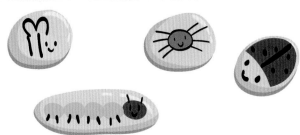

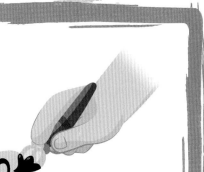

Step 1

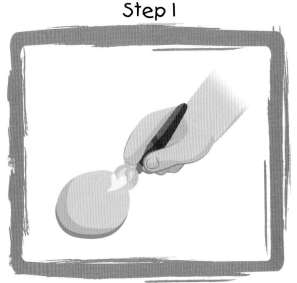

To make the bee, paint a yellow oval shape onto a round pebble.

Step 2

Once dry, add stripes, wings and a face with black paint.

Step 3

Paint clear varnish over the rock to protect them from the rain.

Step 4

Create more bugs using different shaped pebbles.

Finger-painting Fun
Magnificent masterpieces at your fingertips.

Step 1

Dip your thumb into some yellow paint.

You will need:

Paper

Paint

Black felt-tip pen

Step 2

Press your thumb onto a piece of paper several times, leaving a space between each thumbprint.

Step 3

Once dry, use a black felt-tip pen to draw on the bee's stripes, wings and eyes. Try to make each bee look different.

Try this!
Get creative and make lots of different bugs, like these.

Super Spotty Bug

A pretty paper spotty bug to decorate your room with.

Step 1

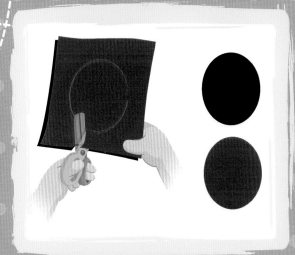

You will need:

Red and black paper   Googly eyes   Glue

Scissors

Holding the red and black paper together, ask an adult to cut out a large oval so that you end up with one red and one black oval of the same size.

Step 3

Step 2

Fig. 1

Ask an adult to cut the black oval about three quarters of the way up, so that you have a semicircle shape, as shown (Fig. 1). This will be the head. Use the remaining black paper to cut out little black circles for the spots, one long strip for the middle line and six strips for the legs.

Stick your spotty bug together, as shown. Be sure to glue the legs to the back of the bug, and the head and spots to the front. Then, glue the googly eyes in place.

Rainy Day Umbrella

Beat boredom on rainy spring days with this origami umbrella.

You will need:

A4 paper   Felt-tip pens   Scissors

Step 1

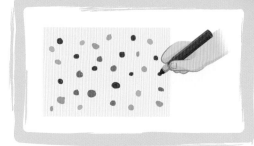

Decorate the paper on both sides with polka dots, stripes or a pattern of your choice.

Step 2

Position the paper so that it is portrait, then fold the paper downwards, in half. With the fold line at the top, draw the shape shown above onto the paper, then ask an adult to cut it out.

Step 3

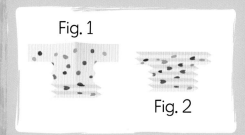

Fig. 1

Fig. 2

Unfold the paper and lay it out flat (Fig. 1). Next, fold the paper horizontally into a concertina shape (Fig. 2).

Step 4

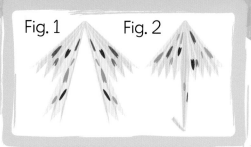

Fig. 1   Fig. 2

Fold the concertina downwards in half with the long stems at the centre (Fig. 1). Pinch the long stems together, then bend the end up, as shown (Fig. 2).

Brilliant Bunting

Decorate your spring garden with this beautiful bunting.

Step 1

Using a felt-tip pen, draw a diamond shape, about 28 cm high and 20 cm wide, onto paper, then ask an adult to cut it out.

You will need:

Material

Scissors

Felt-tip pen

Fabric glue

Paper

Ribbon

Step 2

Ask an adult to help you pin the paper shape to the material, then cut around the shape. Lay the material out flat.

Step 3

Place the ribbon vertically down the middle of the diamond shape. Glue along the edges of one side of the diamond, then fold it over the ribbon, so that it makes a triangle shape.

Step 4

Repeat steps 2-3 until the bunting reaches the length you want. Try to keep an equal distance between each piece of material when attaching it to the ribbon.

Sunshine and Showers

Brighten a grey spring day with this rainbow rain make.

You will need:

Coloured paper

White or grey card

String

Scissors

Sticky tape

Glue

Pencil

Step 1

Draw a cloud shape onto the white or grey card, then ask an adult to cut it out.

Step 2

Draw 18 raindrop shapes onto the coloured paper, then ask an adult to cut them out.

Step 3

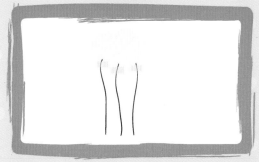

Ask an adult to cut three equal lengths of string and sticky tape them to the back of the cloud.

Step 4

Take two raindrops and glue them together with the string sandwiched between them. Add three raindrops to each string, as shown.

Fork Flowers

Create perfect tulips and dandelions using a fork.

Step 1

You will need: Paper plate
Paper
Paint
Paintbrush
Fork

Pour paint onto a paper plate. Press the back of your fork firmly into the paint, making sure to cover both the base and the prongs.

Step 2

To make a tulip, press the base prongs down onto the paper.

Step 3

To make a dandelion, drag the prongs of the fork across the paper in different directions to make a circular shape.

Step 4

Paint the stems and leaves in green using a paintbrush.

Top tip!
Wash the fork before changing colours so that the paints don't mix.

Rain Cloud Close-ups

The animals are sheltering under a tree from the rain.
Can you work out where each close-up belongs in the picture?

Answers on page 96

Mother Hen

This mother hen wants to reach her chick. Find a path to the chick by stepping on even-numbered flowers only.

Start

Finish

Magic Rainmaker

Create a pitter-patter with this fun musical instrument.

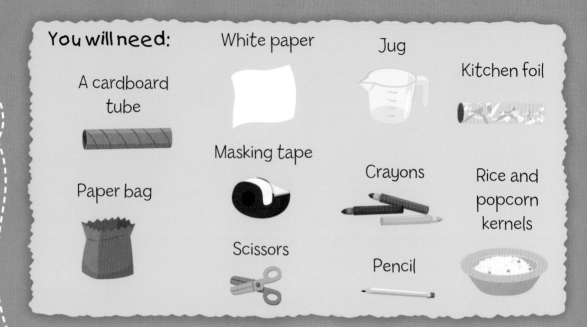

You will need:

A cardboard tube

White paper

Jug

Kitchen foil

Masking tape

Paper bag

Crayons

Rice and popcorn kernels

Scissors

Pencil

Step 1

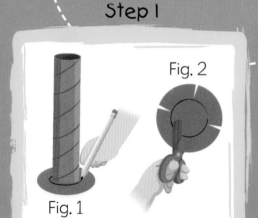

Fig. 2

Fig. 1

Ask an adult to cut out two circles from a paper bag. They should be bigger than the hole of the cardboard tube. Then, draw around the tube in the middle of the paper circle, as shown (Fig. 1), and cut four slits from the edge of the paper to the pencil line, as shown (Fig. 2).

Step 2

Fold one of the paper circles over one end of the cardboard tube. Tape it into place so that one end of the tube is completely sealed up.

Step 3

Take a piece of kitchen foil that is about three times the length of the tube. Scrunch it up into a long snake, then shape it so that it has lots of curves. Push the foil into the tube.

Step 4

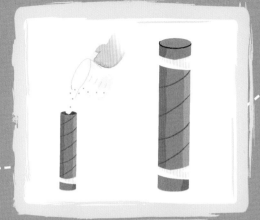

Mix a handful of rice and popcorn kernels in a jug, then pour them into the tube. Seal off the open end using the second circle you made in step 1.

Step 5

Cut a piece of paper big enough to cover the tube. Decorate it with crayons, then tape it around the rainmaker.

Friendship Flower

Spread happiness by giving your friend a pretty flower this spring.

Step 1

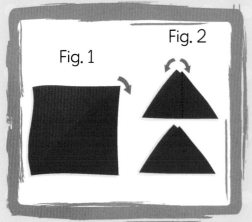

You will need:
1 piece of green paper 15 cm x 15 cm
1 piece of red paper 12 cm x 12 cm
Scissors

For the flower head, take the red paper and fold it in half diagonally (Fig. 1) so it makes a triangle. Open it out and repeat across the opposite corners to make a triangle (Fig. 2).

Step 2

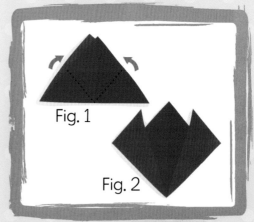

Position the triangle, as shown (Fig. 1). Bring the bottom corners of the triangle up (Fig. 2), so that they are level with the top point, as shown (Fig. 2).

Step 3

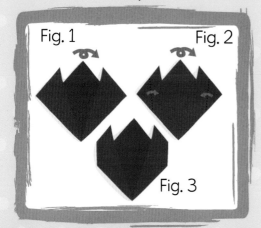

Turn the folded paper over (Fig. 1). Now fold the outside corners in, as shown (Fig. 2). Then turn the folded paper over again (Fig. 3).

Step 4

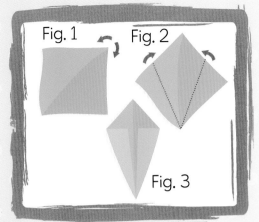

Fig. 1 Fig. 2

Fig. 3

For the stem, take the green paper and fold in half diagonally (Fig. 1). Open it out again and fold the outer corners into the centre fold line as shown (Fig. 2) to create a kite shape (Fig. 3).

Step 5

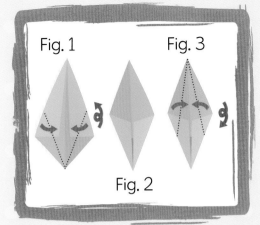

Fig. 1 Fig. 3

Fig. 2

Turn the folded paper upside down, then fold the outer corners into the centre line (Fig. 1). Now you have a diamond shape (Fig. 2). Turn it upside down again, then fold the outer corners into the centre line (Fig. 3).

Step 6

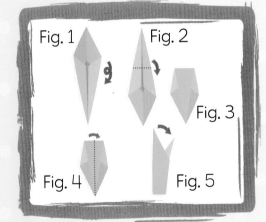

Fig. 1 Fig. 2

Fig. 3

Fig. 4 Fig. 5

Turn the stem upside down (Fig. 1). Fold the stem in half horizontally (Fig. 2), so that the two points meet at the bottom (Fig. 3). Now fold the stem in half vertically (Fig. 4). Slightly pull the narrow stem away (Fig. 5).

Step 7

To attach the flower head to the stem, ask an adult to cut a very small amount off the bottom of your flower, to create a hole for the stem. Slot the stem into the hole to complete the flower.

Doodle Dots

Something is floating through the sky. Connect the
dots to reveal what it is, then use your pens to decorate it.

9 10
8
11
12
7
13
6
14
5
15
4
16
17
3   18
2   19
1   20

Answer on page 96

Bunny Brothers

These bunny brothers all look the same, except for one.
Can you work out which bunny is different from the rest?

Lost and Found

There's something not quite right about the bowl of toys below.
Can you work out where each missing item fits in the picture?

Finger Puppet Fun

Make these cute finger friends and put on a springtime show.

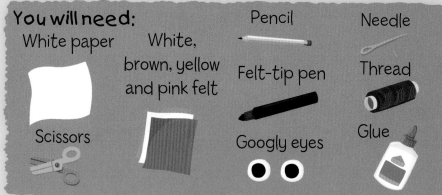

You will need:

White paper

White, brown, yellow and pink felt

Pencil

Felt-tip pen

Needle

Thread

Scissors

Googly eyes

Glue

Step 1

Bunny   Chick   Lamb

Draw the shapes above onto paper. Make sure they are just slightly bigger than your finger. Ask an adult to cut out the shapes.

Step 2

Place the bunny shape onto a piece of brown felt and draw around it to make two bunnies. Ask an adult to cut out the shapes.

Step 3

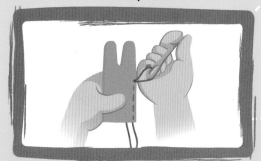

Ask an adult to help you sew together the two shapes. Leave the bottom edge open.

Step 4

Draw a face with the felt-tip pen, then glue on the googly eyes. For the bunny, cut out pink shapes to stick onto the ears. Repeat steps 2-4 to make the chick and lamb.

Mixing Paints

Create your own colour palette by mixing different paints.

Step 1

You will need pink and brown paint to create this pretty tree. To make pink, add a very small amount of red paint to white paint and mix it together. To make brown, mix up equal parts of red, blue and yellow.

You will need:

Paint   Paintbrush   Paper

Why not try these colour combinations, too?

Red + Yellow = Orange

Blue + Yellow = Green

Blue + Red = Purple

Step 2

Paint your tree trunk in brown, as shown. Give it lots of big, winding branches.

Step 3

Dip your finger into the pink paint and use your fingertip to add pretty blossom to the tree.

Perfect Picnic

This is a delicious fruity treat, perfect for a spring party or picnic.

Step 1

Ask an adult to cut the melon into chunks, the grapes into halves and to cut the tops off the strawberries. Peel the satsuma and break it into segments.

You will need:

Melon   Seedless grapes   Strawberries   Skewers
Satsuma   Spoon   Chocolate

Remember! Always ask an adult to help you when using the oven.

Step 2

Add the pieces of melon, strawberry, grape and satsuma onto each skewer.

Step 3

Break the chocolate up into chunks and ask an adult to melt it in a glass bowl over a saucepan of boiling water. Finally, drizzle the melted chocolate over your fruity skewers.

Cloudy Rainbow

Add a splash of colour to your room with this 3D cloud.

Step 1

Draw a big cloud shape onto the card, then ask an adult to cut it out.

You will need:

White card Tissue paper Scissors

Cotton wool Pencil Glue

Step 2

Glue pieces of cotton wool to the front of the cloud shape until it is fully covered.

Step 3

Ask an adult to cut a strip from each of the coloured pieces of paper. Try to keep all the strips the same size.

Step 4

Glue the colourful strips along the bottom of the back of the cloud, as shown.

Happy Deer

This fawn and mummy deer are playing in the meadow.
Use your best pens to decorate the spring picture.

Spring Chicks

Cheep, cheep! These cute chicks have just hatched. Can you work out which close-up doesn't belong in the picture?

a

b

c

d

Mr Fox

This fox is ready for his portrait to be painted.
Copy the picture, square-by-square, then decorate it.

Answer on page 96

Bunny Mobile

Make this cute bunny mobile to hang up in your bedroom.

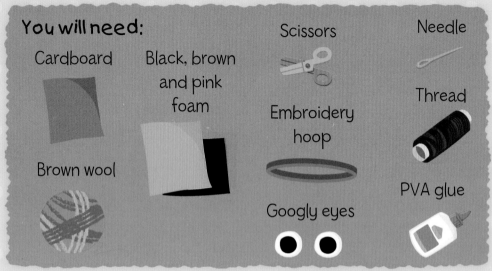

You will need:

Cardboard

Black, brown and pink foam

Brown wool

Scissors

Embroidery hoop

Googly eyes

Needle

Thread

PVA glue

Step 1

Follow the steps from page 18 to make three large pom-poms. Next, repeat the same steps using a small cardboard 'donut' to make three smaller pom-poms.

Step 2

Take one large and one small pom-pom, then ask an adult to sew them together using a needle and thread.

Step 3

Draw the shapes shown above onto the brown, black and pink foam. The pink foam shapes should be smaller than the brown foam shapes. Ask an adult to cut them out.

Step 4

Glue the pink foam shapes onto the brown foam shapes. Next, glue the ears, black nose and googly eyes onto the small pom-pom, as shown.

Step 5

Repeat steps 1-4 twice so that you have three pom-pom bunnies. Ask an adult to sew a 30 cm length of thread to each bunny, then tie them to the embroidery hoop, with equal distance between them.

Step 6

Ask an adult to cut two 50 cm lengths of wool. Tie each length of wool to opposite sides of the embroidery hoop, then tie the loose ends together at the top to make a loop.

Picnic Invitations

Invite your friends to a spring party with these cool invitations.

Step 1

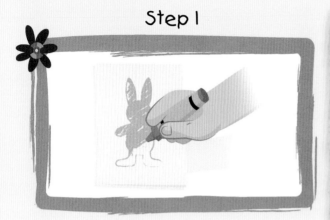

Fold the card in half. Draw a bunny onto the card and colour it in.

You will need:

Card

Crayons

Black felt-tip pen

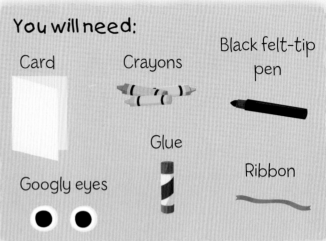

Glue

Ribbon

Googly eyes

Step 2

Glue on some googly eyes, as shown, then draw a triangle nose and a smile.

Step 3

Tie the ribbon into a bow and glue it onto the bunny, under the chin.

Try this! Try other designs, such as eggs and daffodils, using sequins to decorate.

Chocolate Nests

Make these tasty chocolate nests, perfect for sleepovers.

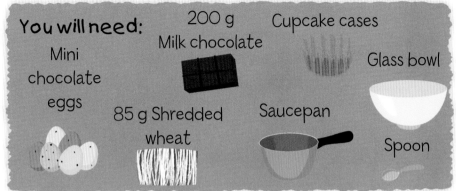

You will need:

Mini chocolate eggs

200 g Milk chocolate

Cupcake cases

Glass bowl

85 g Shredded wheat

Saucepan

Spoon

Step 1

Break the chocolate into small chunks, then ask an adult to melt it in a glass bowl over a saucepan of boiling water.

Step 2

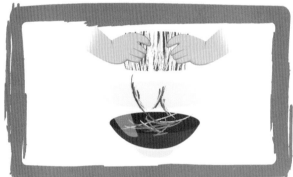

Crush the shredded wheat into small pieces and add it to the bowl of melted chocolate. Mix together until all the shredded wheat is covered.

Step 3

Spoon the mixture into cupcake cases. Add three mini chocolate eggs on top of the nests, then place them in the fridge to set.

Up, Up and Away

Rose, Tom and Megan's kites are tangled up. Follow the lines to work out which kite belongs to each friend.

Answers on page 96

Bobbing Boat

This little toy boat is sailing on the lake. Use your best pens to add a cool design, then colour in the picture.

Daffodil Display

Make this pretty daffodil to display in your window.

Step 1

Paint the paper plate yellow and the cardboard tubes orange.

You will need:

Paper plate   Scissors   Green craft foam   Sticky tape

Cardboard tube   Paint   Paintbrush   Green pipe cleaners

Step 2

Once dry, paint an orange circle in the middle of the paper plate and ask an adult to cut around the edges, as shown.

Step 3

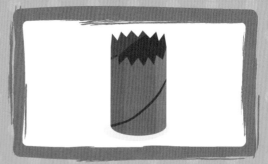

Ask an adult to cut a zigzag line around one edge of the cardboard tube.

Step 4

Using sticky tape, attach the cardboard tube to the front of the flower and the green pipe cleaner to the back.

Step 5

Ask an adult to cut leaf shapes from the green foam. Wrap the end of the leaf around the pipe cleaner, then sticky tape it in place. Display the flower in a jar.

Pretty Shelves

Brighten up your bookshelves with these cool cloud decorations.

Step 1

Draw a cloud shape onto the card. Repeat as many times as you like, remembering to keep an even number. Ask an adult to cut the shapes out.

You will need:

Coloured card

Scissors

String

Glue

Step 2

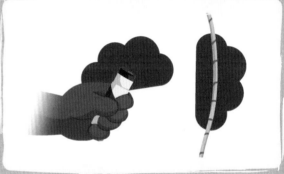

Take two cloud shapes and glue them together with the string sandwiched between them.

Step 3

Continue to add clouds to your string by repeating step 2, until it reaches the desired length. Hang the decorated string along your bookshelf to finish.

Try this!

Why not try adding glitter or sequins to the clouds to make them sparkle?

Super Star Wind Chime

This is a brilliant rainbow decoration to hang in your garden.

Step 1

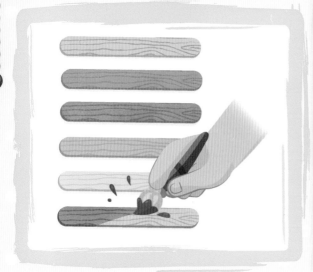

Paint the lollipop sticks in different colours, then leave to dry.

You will need:

Paint

PVA glue

6 Wooden lollipop sticks

Thread

Plastic beads

Large plastic beads

Scissors

Paintbrush

Step 2

Glue the lollipop sticks into two separate triangle shapes. Once dry, place one triangle on top of the other and position as shown. Glue into place.

Step 3

Ask an adult to cut four lengths of thread, about 50 cm long. Tie a knot at the end of each piece.

Step 4

Thread a large bead onto the thread and tie it in place. Next, thread the smaller beads on until the thread is halfway full, leaving 25 cm spare at the top.

Step 5

Add a final large bead and tie it in place. Repeat step 4 to create two more beaded threads. Make a fourth strand leaving only 10 cm of thread at the end.

Step 6

Thread the three shorter threads through the holes of the star, as shown. Next, pull the longer thread through the centre of the star. Tie the four threads together at the top. The lollipop stick star should sit on the big beads.

Step 7

Thread the four tied threads through one large bead and tie it in place to finish. Hang the wind chime from a tree and listen as the beads bump together in the wind.

Spring Shadows

These little animals are making shadowy shapes.
Can you work out which shadow belongs to each animal?

Little Ducklings

The mischievous ducklings are playing hide-and-seek.
How many ducklings can you spot in the picture below?

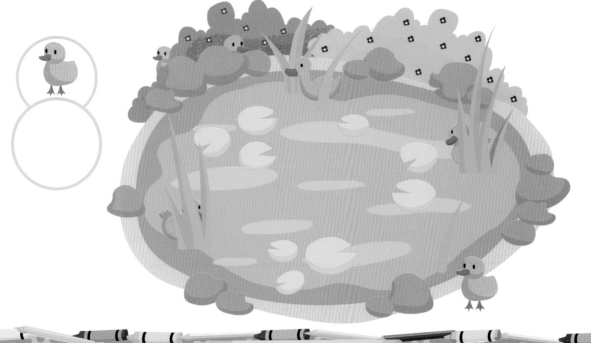

Answers on page 96

Spring Surprise

There's a spring surprise hiding in the picture below.
Finish the picture using the correct colours to reveal what it is.

Answer on page 96

Yummy Cookies

These yummy cookies are perfect for a spring tea party.

You will need:

225 g Caster sugar

300 g Plain flour

200 g Butter

1 tsp Vanilla extract

1 Egg

1 tsp Baking powder

Plastic flower-shaped cookie cutter

Baking tray

Wooden spoon

Rolling pin

Mixing bowl

Cooling rack

Step 1

Mix the butter and sugar together in a mixing bowl until creamy.

Step 2

Add the flour and baking powder into the bowl, then mix it together. Next, add the egg and vanilla and mix again. If it gets too tough, use your hands.

Step 3

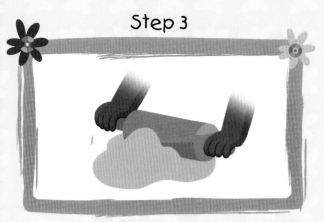

Put the mixture onto a floured surface. Roll it out with a rolling pin until it's about 2 cm thick.

Step 4

Cut the dough with the cookie cutter. When you run out of enough dough to cut, gather the dough in a ball and roll it out again.

Step 5

Place the cookies onto a greased baking tray. Ask an adult to put the cookies in the oven at 160 degrees for 10-20 minutes.

Step 6

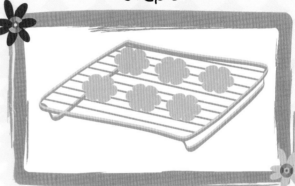

When the edges turn golden, ask an adult to take them out and place the cookies onto a cooling rack to cool.

Duckling Toothbrush Holder

Make this cute duckling to hold your toothbrush.

Step 1

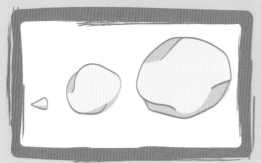

Roll a piece of clay into a big ball and a small ball, then make a small cone shape for the beak.

You will need:

An old toothbrush

Air-drying clay

Paint

Paintbrush

Googly eyes

Step 2

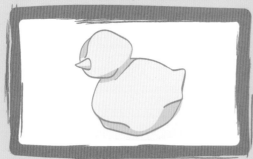

Once the clay is dry, assemble the pieces of clay together, as shown. Next, use your fingers to press out a tail shape.

Step 4

Use the toothbrush to make a deep hole in the top of the duckling, then remove it for the clay to dry. Once dry, paint the duckling yellow with an orange beak.

Step 3

Press the googly eyes into the clay.

Rainbow Butterfly

This brilliant butterfly is colourful and easy to make.

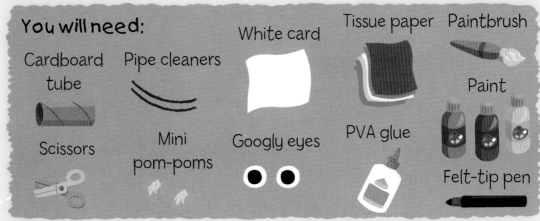

You will need:

Cardboard tube

Pipe cleaners

White card

Tissue paper

Paintbrush

Paint

Scissors

Mini pom-poms

Googly eyes

PVA glue

Felt-tip pen

Step 1

Fold the card in half. Along the fold line, draw a butterfly wing, as shown, then ask an adult to cut it out.

Step 2

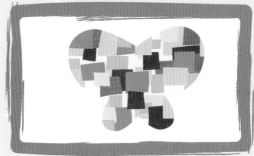

Unfold the butterfly, then glue pieces of tissue paper all over it. Leave to dry.

Step 3

Paint your cardboard tube. Once dry, glue the wings to the back, then glue on the googly eyes and draw a mouth.

Step 4

Glue a pom-pom to the end of each pipe cleaner, then glue them to the inside of the cardboard tube.

Wonderful Woods

All the leaves on the trees grow back in spring.
Finish the picture using your best pens.

Yummy Snacks

No spring picnic is complete without lots of sweet treats.
Can you match up each item to its pair?

Answers on page 96

Bunny Dress-up

Dress up and play bouncing bunnies with these fun ears.

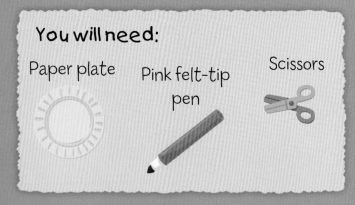

You will need:

Paper plate   Pink felt-tip pen   Scissors

Step 1

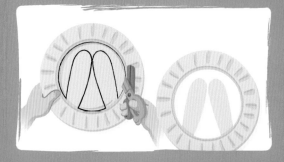

Draw the shape shown above onto the paper plate, then ask an adult to cut it out.

Step 2

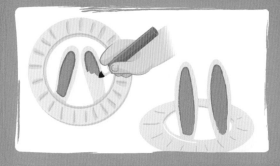

Colour pink shapes onto the ears, then fold them up.

Step 3

Wear your bunny hat with pride.

Handy Chicken

Create this cute chicken masterpiece with your handprint.

You will need:

Paint

Black felt-tip pen

Paintbrush

Paper

Try this!
See what other animals you can make using your handprint.

Step 1

Paint your palm and fingers yellow, then press your hand onto the paper, leaving behind a yellow handprint. Leave it to dry and wash your hand.

Step 2

Paint a beak and wattle with red paint, then draw on the eyes and feet with a felt-tip pen. Leave to dry.

Neat Notelets

Make little spring cards to send to your friends.

Step 1

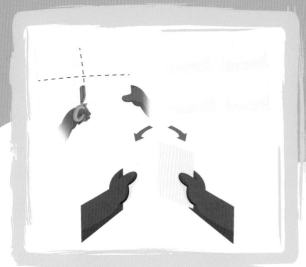

Ask an adult to cut a piece of card into quarters, then fold each quarter in half.

You will need:

Pencil

Card

Coloured paper

Scissors

Glue

Step 2

Draw the shapes shown above onto the coloured paper, then ask an adult to cut them out. Stick one of the shapes to the front of a notelet with glue.

Step 3

Repeat step 2 for the remaining three cards. Don't forget to write messages inside.

Bouncing Bunny

Create a masterpiece with these super bunny paw prints.

Step 1

Ask an adult to cut a potato in half and cut a paw print into it, about 1 cm deep.

You will need:

A potato   Paper   Paintbrush

Paint

Step 2

Paint the paw print shape on the potato, then press it down onto the paper to create a paw print.

Step 3

Repeat across the page to make it look like a bunny trail.

Try this!
Experiment when creating the stamp. What other paw prints can you make?

Egg Code Cracker

These chocolate eggs are all jumbled up. Can you work out where each of the missing eggs belong in the sequences below?

Missing eggs:

Spring Sudoku

Match the missing items to the squares. Each item can only appear once in every row, column and group of coloured squares.

Answers on page 96

Egg Basket

This basket is full of delicious chocolate eggs.
Decorate the picture using your best pens.

Pencil Topper

Make this cute bunny to keep you company whilst writing.

You will need:

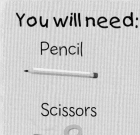

Pencil

Scissors

Googly eyes

PVA glue

Grey, black and pink craft foam

Step 1

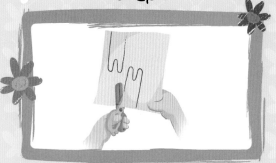

Draw two bunny shapes, as shown, onto craft foam, then ask an adult to cut them out.

Step 2

Glue around the edges of one bunny, leaving the bottom edge open, then stick the second bunny on top.

Step 3

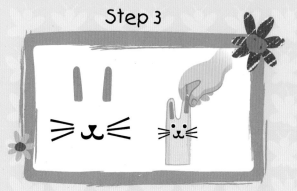

Ask an adult to cut a nose, mouth and whiskers from the black foam and ear shapes from the pink foam. Glue them in place, as shown, then glue on the googly eyes.

Step 4

Dab glue onto the end of the pencil and place the pencil inside the bunny. Next, glue the bottom edges of the bunny and press them together to seal the edges.

Crinkly Caterpillar

Play wiggly caterpillars with this fun straw puppet.

You will need:

White and black paper

Sticky tape

Drinking straws

Glue

Scissors

Long strip of green paper

Black felt-tip pen

Step 1

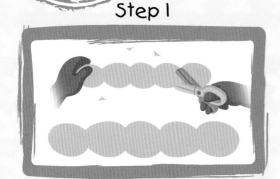

Carefully cut a rounded shape at either end of the green paper strip. Cut some rounded 'v' shapes along the length of the paper strip to make a bumpy caterpillar shape, as shown.

Step 2

Fold the paper strip backwards and forwards to make a concertina shape, then open out the strip.

Step 3

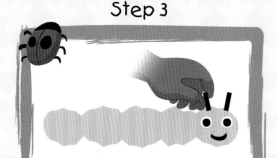

Cut two small circles from the white paper and glue them on for eyes. Cut two small strips from the black paper and glue them on for the antennae. Draw pupils and a mouth with the black felt-tip pen.

Step 4

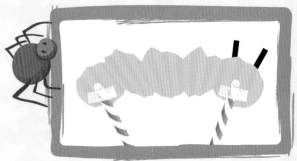

To complete your caterpillar, stick the straws to the back, at either end using sticky tape.

Hatching Chick

Play peek-a-boo with this cute hatching chick.

Step 1

Cut an egg shape out of the white card and a smaller rounded oval shape from the yellow card, as shown. Next, cut a small triangle from the orange card for the chick's beak.

You will need:

Split pin

Scissors

Yellow, orange and white card

Googly eyes

Glue

Remember! Always ask an adult to help when using scissors.

Step 2

Cut a zigzag all the way across the egg, about two thirds of the way up. Overlap the top and bottom sections slightly, then attach them together at the side with a split pin. Make sure it's loose enough so that the egg can be opened and closed.

Step 3

Stick the yellow oval shape to the back of the bottom part of the egg, so that it looks like the head is peeking out. Next, glue the googly eyes and beak in place.

Folding Flower

Fold these funky flowers to create a stylish bouquet.

You will need:

Tissue paper	Green pipe cleaners	Scissors

Step 1

Fold a piece of tissue paper in half, then fold it backwards and forwards to make a concertina shape.

Step 2

Fold the concertina in half, then wrap a pipe cleaner around the middle. Twist the ends of the pipe cleaner together, then shape one end of the pipe cleaner into a leaf shape, as shown.

Step 3

Ask an adult to trim the edges of the concertina into a rounded shape, to look like petals.

Step 4

Gently pull the paper apart, then fluff it up so that it looks like a flower.

Brilliant Bird Feeder

Recycle a plastic bottle to bring lots of birds to your garden.

You will need:

A clear plastic bottle

Coloured tissue paper

PVA glue

Paintbrush

Stick

Bird seed

Scissors

String

Step 1

Cut off the top of the plastic bottle, then cut the front section out, rounding the edges, as shown.

Step 2

Cut the tissue paper into small squares.

Step 3

Stick the tissue paper squares to the inside of the plastic bottle with PVA glue, until the entire inside of the bottle is covered. Leave to dry.

Step 4

Ask an adult to cut two small holes on either side of the feeder near the bottom, as shown. Thread the stick through the holes. This will be a perch for the birds to stand on.

Step 5

Cut a further two holes at the top of the bottle, as shown. Thread the string through both holes, then tie the loose ends together to create a loop. Fill it up with bird seed, then hang from a branch.

93

Paper Bag Nest

Keep your chocolate eggs safe in this paper nest.

Step 1

Ask an adult to cut off the top of a brown paper bag.

You will need:

Brown paper bag   Scissors   Green tissue paper

Step 2

Scrunch the bottom of the bag down.

Step 3

Ask an adult to cut the top part of the bag into strips, as shown, then cut the green tissue paper into strips.

Step 4

Put the green strips into the nest, then arrange the brown strips from step 3 around the outside of the nest.

Step 5

Place your chocolate eggs inside.

Happy Bunnies

Make a cute chain of bunnies holding hands.

You will need:

Paper

Scissors

Crayons

Pencil

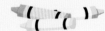

Step 1

Fold the paper backwards and forwards to make a concertina.

Step 2

Draw a bunny onto the front section of the paper. Make all four paws touch the edges, as shown.

Step 3

Ask an adult to cut out the bunny, making sure they do not cut along the folds at the ends of the paws.

Step 4

Unfold the paper to reveal a chain of bunny rabbits holding paws. Decorate each bunny differently, then hang them up.

Answers

Page 8: Moo Meadow

Page 9: Happy Lambs
Shadow b

Page 9: Bunny Mischief
Bunny a

Page 15: Which Weather?
a-3, b-1, c-2

Page 20: Fluffy Friends
Character a is the odd one out, because he doesn't have wings.

Page 20: Eggs for Everyone
a-2, b-3, c-1

Page 26: Magnificent Maze

Page 32: Wonderful Wildlife
Grid d

Page 33: Broken Eggshells
a-n, b-o, c-p, d-f, e-k, g-j, h-i, l-m

Page 36: Cool Creepy-crawlies

Page 37: Jumping Jigsaw
a-2, b-5, c-4, d-1, e-3

Page 50: Rain Cloud Close-ups
a-2b, b-4b, c-5d, d-3e

Page 51: Mother Hen

Page 56: Doodle Dots
A hot-air balloon.

Page 57: Bunny Bother
f is the odd one out.

Page 57: Lost and Found
a-4, b-1, c-3, d-2, e-5

Page 63: Spring Chicks
Close-up b

Page 68: Up, Up and Away
a-2, b-1, c-3

Page 74: Spring Shadows
a-3, b-4, c-1, d-2

Page 74: Little Ducklings
There are six ducklings in the picture.

Page 75: Spring Surprise
A spring bonnet

Page 81: Yummy Snacks
a-2, b-1, c-6, d-4, e-3, f-7, g-5, h-8

Page 86: Egg Code Cracker
1-a, 2-b and c

Page 86: Spring Sudoku
a-4, b-3, c-1, d-2